All abou

The Jurassic Coast

by Robert Westwood
Inspiring Places Publishing
2 Down Lodge Close
Alderholt
Fordingbridge
SP6 3JA

ISBN 978-0-9955964-0-5
www.inspiringplaces.co.uk

JURASSICCOAST
**QUALITY
BUSINESS**

Contents

Introduction - some basic facts

The Jurassic Coast starts at Orcombe Point near Exmouth, Devon and ends at Studland Bay, Dorset – about 95 miles.

It is only a narrow strip of coastline, roughly from the average low tide mark to the top of the cliffs, or the back of the beach where there are no cliffs. Its boundaries do not include the towns of Exmouth, Sidmouth, Seaton, Lyme Regis, West Bay, Weymouth, Portland Port or Swanage – basically it consists of long, thin stretches of undeveloped coastline.

The ownership of the coast is in a variety of hands; the National Trust, Crown Estate, Ministry of Defence, local and national authorities, large private estates and small landowners. The World Heritage Site is managed by the Jurassic Coast Team, a collaboration between the Jurassic Coast Trust (a registered charity) and local authorities.

The rocks of the Jurassic Coast are all sediments (see page 12), aged between roughly 250 and 65 million years old.

What is a World Heritage Site?

A World Heritage Site is somewhere that has been specifically recognised by the United Nations Educational Scientific and Cultural Organisation (UNESCO) as being of special significance culturally, scientifically, historically or in some other way. These sites are protected by international treaties and are considered by the United Nations to be important to the collective interests of humanity.

Red sandstones at Budleigh Salterton.

Why is this coastline so important?

One of the main reasons why this coastline is a World Heritage Site is the fossils found in its rocks. These fossils tell the story of life on Earth during the 185 million years of the Mesozoic Era. It is an amazing story; just before the era began life had suffered a terrible catastrophe. Known as the "Great Dying", around ninety-five per cent of marine species and seventy per cent of terrestrial species died out. The cause is still debated, but it seems likely climate changes induced by huge volcanic eruptions may have played a large part. The end of the era, around 65 million years ago, saw another mass extinction event, this time possibly the result of a meteorite impact. In between these two mass extinctions life recovered and flourished

Worbarrow Bay on the Isle of Purbeck. The foreground and tilted layers on the left of the picture are the Portland and Purbeck limestones, while the cliffs at the far end of the bay are of the Chalk. Sandwiched in between are the softer sands and clays of the Cretaceous Wealden Series.

in the warm tropical climates that came to dominate, particularly from the start of the Jurassic Period. Many weird and wonderful species swam in the oceans and walked through the verdant forests and they have left their fascinating stories in the rocks along the coast of east Devon and Dorset.

The coastline also tells us much about the processes that have shaped and formed it. Wonderful features like Lulworth Cove and Chesil Beach have been created by the interactions of the sea and atmosphere with the nature and structure of the rocks. Other features in the rocks tell us about ancient environments. Coastal landslips are a common result of this interaction and although sometimes hazardous and unsightly, have had the useful effect of revealing many more fossils for investigation, and thus greatly enhancing our knowledge of life in the Mesozoic Era.

Geological time

It is generally agreed that the Earth is around four and a half billion years old. Geologists divide this great span of time into eons, eras and periods, in descending order of length. The divisions are based on the nature of life around at any time and the first eon, the Hadean, represents the time before life began and ends around four billion years ago. We are now in the Phanerozoic Eon, which began between six hundred and five hundred million years ago, and is characterised by the appearance of the first easily recognisable fossils. This eon is divided into three eras, the Palaeozoic (meaning old life), the Mesozoic and the Cenozoic. Most rocks we find on the Earth's surface were formed in the Phanerozoic, and in Britain, the vast majority are from the latter two eras. Why is this? Why are most of the rocks we find relatively young compared to the age of the Earth? The answer lies in the constant recycling of the Earth's crust. 'Plates' of the crust are moving, driven by energy from the planet's hot interior. New rocks are formed by volcanic activity, mountains are pushed up which are then weathered and eroded by the atmosphere, leading to the formation of new sedimentary rocks in lakes and oceans.

Why Jurassic?

The rocks of the Jurassic Coast were formed in the Mesozoic Era which comprises three periods, the Triassic, Jurassic and Cretaceous. So the Jurassic is only one of three periods of geological time represented in this world heritage site – but a name had to be chosen and "Jurassic" is the best known. The name comes from the Jura mountains of France and Switzerland where limestones from this period were first identified and described by Alexander von Humboldt.

Era	Period	Age my
Cenozoic — Quaternary →	**Neogene**	2.3
		23
	Palaeogene	
		65
Mesozoic	**Cretaceous**	
		145
	Jurassic	
		199
	Triassic	
		251
Upper Palaeozoic	**Permian**	
		299
	Carboniferous	
		359
	Devonian	
		416
Lower Palaeozoic	**Silurian**	443
	Ordovician	
		488
	Cambrian	
		542

Picture opposite page: A fossil ammonite sits on a block of limestone on the shore at Kimmeridge. It lived perhaps 140-150 million years ago and will soon be washed back into the sea where it may become part of a future sedimentary rock.

The Age of Rocks - how do we know?

We are told that an ammonite we find on the beach at Lyme Regis may have lived around 180 million years ago. How can we possibly know that? The first thing to note is that there is nothing about that ammonite, or indeed the rocks from which it came, that tell us anything about its absolute age. Since the early days of geology in the nineteenth century, geologists have developed great expertise in the art of relative dating. Using such elementary reasoning as a rock layer must have been deposited before the layer on top of it, as well as more sophisticated techniques, through exhaustive and detailed detective work, they have been able to place the rock strata of the British Isles in relative order of age. Fossils have been a major part of this, at each point in the geological history of the Phanerozoic Eon (see page 6) there has been a distinct collection of

This fossil ammonite at Kimmeridge lies under water as the tide rises. It rests on what was the bottom of the Jurassic sea where it lived over 150 million years ago.

biomes that have left a fossil record. This can help correlate different rocks from different regions as the same age.

So we can tell the relative age of rocks; we know that the red rocks of east Devon are older than the Chalk, but how much older, when were they all formed? To obtain an absolute age scientists basically use a technique called radio-isotope dating. This relies on the fact that radioactive elements decay at a known, measurable rate and therefore, the relative proportion of that element will tell us how long it has been decaying. Since sedimentary rocks are formed from bits and pieces of older rocks, this technique is of no use in determining their date of formation, but it can be used to calculate the age of igneous or volcanic rocks, telling us how long it has been since that rock crystallised from a molten state. Geologists can then correlate that rock with other layers and eventually build up a more complete picture of the actual age of rocks across Britain.

Geological Map of the Jurassic Coast

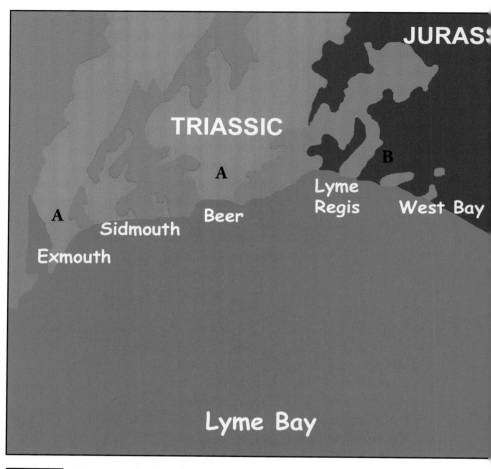

A — Triassic rocks, largely sandstones and mudstones deposited in desert environments by seasonal rivers and lakes, and by the action of wind in the arid landscape.

B — Jurassic, mainly marine, sediments. Clays, shales, sandstones and limestones deposited in fairly shallow seas teeming with life. Land was often not far away.

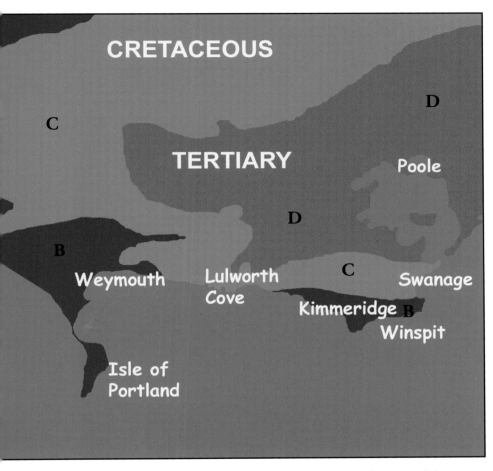

| C | The Cretaceous - After a period of erosion when this part of the world was land once more, the sea returned and deposited a variety of sediments; sandstones, clays and finally the enigmatic Chalk. |

| D | The Tertiary Era - After the great extinction the environment changed relatively rapidly and a succession of sediments from rivers, river deltas and shallow seas were laid down. |

Sediments

All of the rocks found on the Jurassic Coast are sedimentary rocks, many were formed from the weathered bits of older rocks deposited by the action of the sea, rivers and wind. Most are marine, sediments that were laid down on the sea bed, typically a shallow sea, but a significant proportion are continental, laid down in lakes, by rivers, by wind, and in coastal lagoons. Sandstones, clays and silts are typical of these sorts of sedimentary rocks, the size of the grains reflecting a sorting process whereby larger particles sink to the bottom first and only fine particles are carried out further from the shore.

Another group of sediments is intimately associated with life; limestones contain a large proportion of calcium carbonate, a mineral used by many organisms for their hard parts. As sediment is being compacted by the weight above this can precipitate out and act as a cement, binding particles together.

Sandstones

A sandstone is a rock composed of sand sized grains (1/16 to 2mm diameter) loosely or strongly cemented together. The grains are usually of quartz or

Sandstone at Ladram Bay, Devon.

Dark shale gradually turns to limestone, Kimmeridge, Dorset.

feldspar as these two minerals are the most resistant to weathering. They can form in a variety of environments, in deserts, lakes, rivers and on the sea bed. The red sandstones of East Devon are desert sandstones, deposited in seasonal lakes and rivers or by wind.

Clays

These are very fine grained sediments with particles of less than 0.002mm. They are composed of clay minerals which are formed by the weathering of feldspars and other minerals found in igneous and volcanic rocks. Clays are often deposited in relatively deep seas as the fine particles can drift further from the shore. When compacted clays, whose minerals have a flat, two dimensional structure, can turn into shales that are easily split along parallel layers; and when further compacted and heated during metamorphism can become slate.

Limestones

Limestones form in relatively shallow waters and are indicative of an environment rich in life. Many organisms have evolved to use the dissolved salts in sea water to make their hard parts from calcium carbonate. Some limestones are formed as the broken bits of dead organisms become cemented together as they are compacted on the sea bed. The dissolved calcium carbonate in sea water provides this cement, due largely to the fact that its solubility increases with increased pressure. As grains of calcium carbonate (typically shell fragments) are squeezed together they begin to dissolve around the points of contact; as this solution migrates to spaces between the grains it precipitates again, cementing the grains together.

Chalk

Chalk is a common, yet somewhat mysterious, sedimentary rock. Unlike other sediments, there is no place on Earth today where we can say for sure that chalk is forming. Pure chalk is almost entirely calcium carbonate, formed from the remains of microscopic planktonic organisms. Chief among these are coccolithophores, tiny organisms that secrete plates of calcium carbonate for protection. These beautifully detailed discs are only about three thousandths of a millimetre in diameter and are constantly replaced. In some tropical oceans today the sea is milky white as millions of these plates gradually sink to the bottom. Just think how many billions of these creatures contributed to the Chalk which is hundreds of feet thick in places. The mystery about chalk is that some layers contain almost no terrigenous material, that is, sand or clay particles. There must have been no sediment being carried into the seas where the Chalk formed – a very unusual situation. Some have speculated that it may have been deposited in an ocean bordered by a waterless desert where there were no rivers to bring sediment.

The Chalk at Swyre Head.

Pangaea

We know that the continents are not fixed on the Earth's surface, the crust is divided into several 'plates' which move, driven by the heat energy of the Earth's interior. At a number of times in the Earth's history the continents have coincidentally converged to form one 'supercontinent'. The last time this happened was at the end of the Palaeozoic Era, the starting point for the rocks of the Jurassic Coast. So, the Triassic Period starts with all the world's landmass in a giant continent that has come to be called 'Pangaea' (Greek for 'entire Earth'). This would have been a very different Earth from the one we know as home today, looked at from space there would have been no white ice caps around the poles and the vast interior of the one landmass would have presented a vibrant red, indicative of an arid desert. Strips of green would have been visible around the coasts as well as perhaps on some mountainous regions. The climate in the interior would have been extreme with huge temperature ranges between summer and winter; and although generally very dry, some areas may have had an intense monsoonal climate.

The red sandstones we now see exposed on the coast of East Devon were formed in this harsh environment. They were deposited in seasonal lakes, by mighty rivers which brought detritus from the wetter mountain ranges onto the plains below or by the action of the wind, building dunes like we see in today's deserts. The evidence for this story is in the rocks and we shall look at some of this in more detail later.

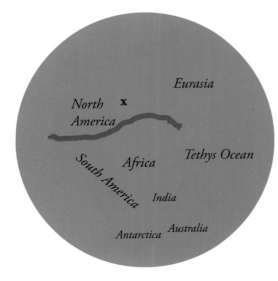

Left: A very rough approximation to what's thought to be the shape of Pangaea at the beginning of the Triassic Period. 'X' marks where the British Isles was situated and the red line where the great continent began to split apart at the beginning of the Jurassic. This caused the mean sea level to rise all over the Earth as the break up of the supercontinent altered the distribution of deep ocean basins.

The Great Extinctions

The period before the Mesozoic Era (the 'Jurassic Coast era') is known as the Permian, and started around 300 million years ago. It was the time of Pangaea, when all the Earth's landmass was concentrated in a giant supercontinent. This huge landmass would have been subject to extreme climate variations, making life difficult for land species. There would also have been relatively little continental shelf, the habitat for the majority of marine plants and animals. At the end of this dramatic period, about 250 million years BP, life on Earth suffered its most devastating mass extinction, known colloquially as 'The Great Dying', when over ninety percent of marine species died out and around seventy percent of land species. The cause of this is still debated and it may have been a combination of circumstances, but one event that may have played a part is intense volcanic activity that saw vast outpourings of lava in what is now Siberia. This activity may have had a dramatic effect on the Earth's climate, with a huge amount of debris in the

atmosphere resulting in global cooling and reducing the ability of plants to photosynthesise.

Just over 65 million years ago another massive episode of volcanic activity (in India) coincided with another great extinction that marked the end of the Mesozoic Era. This may again have contributed to the demise of roughly three quarters of all the plant and animal species on Earth, but many scientists believe it was triggered by the impact of an asteroid some six miles in diameter. The colossal impact possibly occurred near the Yucatan Penisula off the coast of Mexico and would have had a dramatic effect on the Earth's climate. This was the extinction that saw the end of the dinosaurs, the large marine reptiles and the ammonites. Thus the rocks of the Jurassic Coast represent a very special time for the evolution of life on Earth; who knows what direction it would have taken had these two catastrophic extinctions not taken place; we may not have evolved at all.

Some wonderful creatures evolved and flourished between the two extinction events. The large skull is from an Ichthyosaur (courtesy Lyme Regis Museum). They did not survive after the Mesozoic, along with the ammonites and dinosaurs.

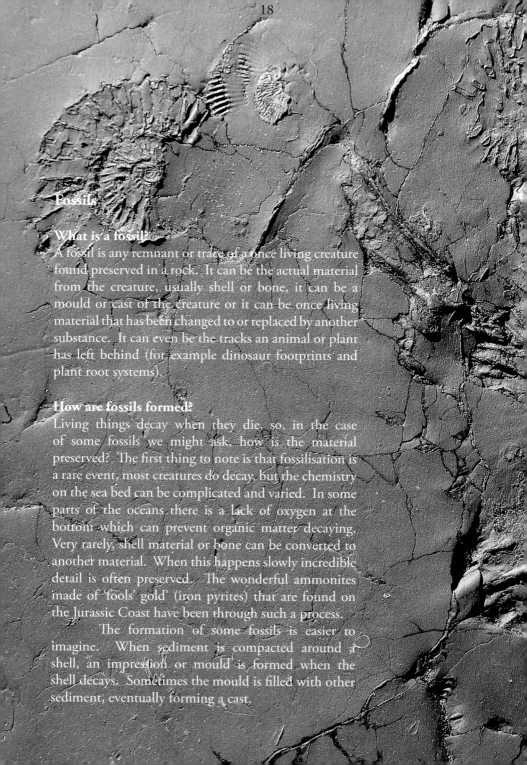

Fossils

What is a fossil?

A fossil is any remnant or trace of a once living creature found preserved in a rock. It can be the actual material from the creature, usually shell or bone, it can be a mould or cast of the creature or it can be once living material that has been changed to or replaced by another substance. It can even be the tracks an animal or plant has left behind (for example dinosaur footprints and plant root systems).

How are fossils formed?

Living things decay when they die, so, in the case of some fossils we might ask, how is the material preserved? The first thing to note is that fossilisation is a rare event, most creatures do decay, but the chemistry on the sea bed can be complicated and varied. In some parts of the oceans there is a lack of oxygen at the bottom which can prevent organic matter decaying. Very rarely, shell material or bone can be converted to another material. When this happens slowly incredible detail is often preserved. The wonderful ammonites made of 'fools' gold' (iron pyrites) that are found on the Jurassic Coast have been through such a process.

The formation of some fossils is easier to imagine. When sediment is compacted around a shell, an impression or mould is formed when the shell decays. Sometimes the mould is filled with other sediment, eventually forming a cast.

These ammonites were found on the beach at Kimmeridge. The large one still has some of its original shell preserved while some of the smaller ones do not and are casts of the original creatures. There were numerous ammonites in this particular layer, perhaps indicating that a change of conditions had caused many to die quite suddenly.

What fossils do we find on the Jurassic Coast?

We have seen that at the end of the era before the rocks of the Jurassic Coast were formed, life on Earth had been devastated, but recovered thanks, partly, to the new marine environments formed by the break up of Pangaea. The remains of these life forms are now in the sediments on the Jurassic Coast, particularly the Jurassic sediments but also in deposits from the later Cretaceous Period.

Most fossils we find in the rocks are from creatures with shells, and many of these are molluscs. Ammonites are marine molluscs as are the bullet shaped belemnites and the many varieties of bivalves. The similar looking brachiopods however are not molluscs but an entirely different group. The top predators in the Jurassic seas were the large marine reptiles like the ichthyosaurs, pliosaurs and plesiosaurs. Their bones are sometimes found and several remarkable skeletons or part skeletons are on display in local museums. The remains of crocodiles are also sometimes found, particularly in the sediments that formed in coastal lagoons towards the end of the Jurassic Period. Here too we sometimes see remains of dinosaurs, or rather the footprints they left in the soft mud of the lagoons. Fish remains are also quite common, but perhaps often overlooked, for it is their teeth that are preserved most easily and these can often be seen seemingly scattered through rocks such as the Purbeck limestones. Echinoderms like sea urchins and starfish are also found in certain formations. All in all there are very many species of fossils in the rocks of the World Heritage Site, but perhaps the ones that catch our attention are ones that did not survive the great extinction at the end of the Cretaceous; the ammonites, marine reptiles and the dinosaurs.

Pictures: Some fossils found on the Jurassic Coast:

1. A belemnite. The bullet shaped fossil is the 'guard', part of the internal skeleton of this marine mollusc.

2. Purbeck limestone full of the shells of bivalve molluscs.

3. A Jurassic fish, 'Dapedium' - courtesy Lyme Regis Museum.

4. Found in a hard, limestone ledge at Kimmeridge, this is probably a bone from a marine reptile.

5. As well as the bivalve centre left of the picture, this piece of Purbeck limestone is full of fossilised worm burrows. Purbeck limestone was formed in a shallow, tropical coastal lagoon - these worms burrowed in its soft mud. The lagoon may have temporarily dried out and when the water returned the burrows filled with sediment.

6. Crinoids, often called 'sea lilies', are not plants but 'echinoderms'. They lived attached to the sea bottom or sometimes floating driftwood from coastal forests. Courtesy Lyme Regis Museum.

Landslips

Landslips may sometimes appear as a blot on a picturesque stretch of coastline, but they are welcomed by the many dedicated fossil hunters who scour Dorset's beaches. The rocks of the Jurassic Coast are particularly prone to landslips and the reason is not hard to understand. In many places along the coast the strata are sloping gently seawards with permeable limestone or chalk layers above impermeable clay. Water soaks through the permeable rocks but, unable to penetrate the layer beneath, forms a lubricated plane between the two rock types. In time gravity does the rest and part of the cliff slides over this slippery layer. Faults in the rocks can also be a major factor, providing planes of weakness and enabling large blocks to break off from the cliffs. In some places the orientation of the strata can be a factor. West of Lulworth Cove in Man O'War Bay, the layers of the Chalk cliffs are vertical and in 2013 a huge block of Chalk broke away from the cliff along these vertical planes of weakness.

It is these landslips, particularly around places like Lyme Regis and Charmouth, that lead to thousands of fossils being released from the rocks. Enthusiasts and professional collectors often swarm around fresh landslips, sometimes at the risk of their own safety. Always follow local advice on such matters, the famous collector Mary Anning was almost killed on a landslip, at an incident that cost the life of her dog.

Picture: Hooken Cliff, Beer, Devon. In March 1790 seven to ten acres of coastline fell roughly two hundred metres. The permeable Chalk and Upper Greensand rest on impermeable Triassic mudstones; water passing through the permeable rocks lubricated the junction with the mudstones.

How does the coast erode?

It has been estimated that cliffs on the Dorset coast are retreating, on average, between twenty and sixty metres per hundred years*. Recent cliff falls such as that east of Durdle Door in 2013 remind us that the shape of the coastline can change dramatically in a human lifetime. The Jurassic Coast is a wonderful place to study the interaction between the processes that weather and erode and the nature and structure of the rocks that form the coastline. While sometimes the processes and geology are complicated, nevertheless it is reasonably easy to pick out some broad principles and general features as we wander along the coast path.

The Dorset coast is the perfect place to appreciate the difference between what are called 'concordant' and 'discordant' coastlines. When the geological strata trend parallel to the coastline this is termed concordant and

Above: Man O'War Bay, east of Durdle Door suffered a major landslip in spring 2013; the sea turned milky-white as the chalk was dissolved by the seawater.
P25, top: Mupe Rocks and Mupe Bay, like Man O'War Bay, a perfect example of a concordant coastline. The Chalk (left of picture) and Portland and Purbeck limestones trend parallel to the coast and form high ground with the softer Wealden Beds forming the low cliffs in Worbarrow Bay in the left distance.
P25, middle left: The sea has cut a notch in the bottom of the cliffs at Burton Bradstock. This will eventually lead to collapse.
P25, middle right: At Durdle Door the sea has cut a platform as the cliffs retreat.
* Andrew Goudie 1995

when they trend at right angles to the coast it is termed discordant. Consider Swanage Bay where the Chalk, Wealden Beds and Purbeck limestones meet the sea at right angles. The softer Wealden Beds have been eroded much faster by the waves while the Chalk and limestones form impressive headlands. By contrast, around Lulworth Cove the strata trend parallel to the coast, in particular the layers of the Portland and Purbeck limestones. These fairly resistant layers form impressive cliffs, but at Lulworth, where the limestones have been breached, the sea has eroded the softer sands and clays behind more quickly, forming the famous, almost circular cove.

The sea erodes the coast in a number of ways. The force of the waves and the rocks, pebbles and other detritus they carry along gradually wear away at the bottom of cliffs, but perhaps a more destructive force is due to the hydraulic action as air is forced into cracks and fissures and compressed. Rocks like limestones and chalk with a high proportion of calcium carbonate are also prone to corrosion.

Folding and Faulting

The Earth's crust is constantly moving, driven by forces generated from the heat of the planet's interior. Looking at the face of the Earth over a long period it would seem as if the continents move; they do, but are riding on the backs of the plates of the crust, which include oceanic as well as continental crust. When plates collide huge forces contort rocks caught in between, sometimes producing mountain chains along the zone of collision. The rock layers of mountain regions are often dramatically folded, and the rocks themselves changed by heat and pressure. Away from the actual collision zone and hence the zone of most intense folding, forces may be transmitted through the crust and produce more gentle deformations. It is these forces that explain why layers of sediments deposited on a horizontal sea floor now form parts of continental landmasses and are sometimes buckled and folded. Although never caught in a region of intense deformation, the rocks of the Jurassic Coast do show many features caused by these earth movements.

Above: These strata at Osmington Mills now lie almost vertical, whereas they were deposited in horizontal layers. Clearly they have been subject to tremendous forces that have folded these layers.

If some regions of the Earth's crust are subject to compressional forces then it stands to reason that other regions will experience tensional forces. This can result in fractures or faults in the crust where sometimes one side slips downwards relative to the other. Faults can also be the result of compression, where one side of the line of fracture is pushed over the other side. These are known as reverse faults or thrusts.

Above: Looking east from Beer Head, Devon. The Chalk suddenly gives way on the coast to red sandstone, despite the layers being almost horizontal. A major fault has dropped the younger Chalk down to the level of the Triassic sandstone.

Left: Dramatic folding in the 'Lulworth Crumple' at Stair Hole, thought to have been caused by gravity collapse as the strata were uplifted and tilted nearly vertical.
Above: A small fault in the sandstones near Orcombe Point has displaced layers by several metres.

The Red Coast

The Triassic Period began just over 250 million years ago and lasted for around 50 million years. Its start was defined, as we have seen, by a dramatic decline in living species and was at a time when all the Earth's landmass was concentrated in the supercontinent of Pangaea. Devon and Dorset were situated within this continent, part of a great, arid desert. Deserts are largely areas where erosion dominates but sediments are deposited by seasonal rivers flowing from mountains and by temporary 'playa' lakes in intermontane (between mountains) basins. Wind blown sediments can also accumulate. It is these types of deposits we find along the coast of East Devon, predominantly sandstones and mudstones coloured red by the oxidation of iron in those ancient desert environments.

The picture shows the cliffs just east of Ladram Bay; Peak Hill is the tall cliff. The lower part of the cliff is composed of the Otter Sandstone which gives way about half way up to the softer Mercia Mudstone; hence the change in angle of the cliff. Peak Hill is actually capped by the Cretaceous Upper Greensand, another instance of the Great Unconformity (see page 37).

The Jurassic Coast starts at Orcombe Point near Exmouth with red sandstones and mudstones of the Aylesbeare Formation; strictly speaking these are Permian in age (the period before the Triassic) and the mudstones were formed in playa lakes while the sandstone layers may have been deposited by wind on dried out lake beds. As we travel eastwards along the coast we see later formations due to the gentle eastwards dip of the rock layers. Following the Aylesbeare Mudstone is the Budleigh Salterton Pebble Beds (see page 31), after which comes the Otter Sandstone, laid down by seasonal rivers and streams flowing across the desert landscape. The final desert deposit is the Mercia Mudstone, again formed in seasonal playa lakes.

There are features we can recognise in these rocks which give us clues to their origin. In the Otter Sandstone for example we often see 'current bedding' where inclined layers of sandstone cut across one another and represent shifting river channels. Layers of gypsum (calcium sulphate) in the mudstones represent evaporite deposits when the lakes dried out.

Current bedding in the Otter Sandstone.

Hard bands of sandstone in the Aylesbeare Mudstone near Orcombe Point.

The Budleigh Salterton Pebble Beds

There is no better place on the Jurassic Coast to appreciate the fact that the Earth's crust is constantly being recycled than Budleigh Salterton. Each pebble in the famous Pebble Beds tells an amazing story. The pebbles are made of quartzite, a type of sandstone made extremely hard by heat and pressure generated as plates of the Earth's crust collided in an episode that generated a formidable mountain range around 400 million years ago. The original sandstone was the product of weathering – perhaps of an even older mountain range. At the beginning of the Triassic Period, about 250 million years ago, the quartzite in the mountains was being eroded and carried northwards by fast rivers that spilled onto desert plains, depositing their load of smooth, rounded quartzite pebbles and forming what would become the Budleigh Salterton Pebble Beds. As we might expect if the rivers were flowing northwards, the pebbles become smaller as we trace the bed northwards. Very rarely a fossil is found in a pebble, not of a creature from the Triassic, but from the time when the original sandstones were formed more than 400 million years ago.

Above: A close up of the Budleigh Salterton Pebble Beds. The pebbles are mostly of quartzite rounded by the action of water. Their size indicates that they must have been carried by fast flowing rivers.

Top and above: The Pebble Beds are clearly visible at the bottom of each photograph. The junction with the overlying sandstone is quite distinct (smaller photograph shows this more clearly), indicating that the powerful rivers that carried the pebbles from the south stopped flowing relatively suddenly. If you visit this site look out for angular pebbles just above the Pebble Beds which are characteristic of weathering by wind, suggesting that the rivers had given way to arid desert conditions.

Above: Honeycomb weathering in sandstone at Budleigh Salterton. This is a phenomenon of coastal regions and it is thought salt, perhaps from sea spray, collects and crystallises in the pores of the sandstone, forcing the grains apart.

The Fossil Beaches - Lyme Regis and Charmouth

Have a look at a geological map of the Jurassic Coast; does it look as if the Jurassic and Cretaceous sediments have spread across the Triassic rocks from the east, ending at roughly the Dorset / Devon border? This is basically what did happen; at the beginning of the Jurassic Period the sea returned to this part of the world and the red rocks of the Triassic's desert landscape were submerged under an ocean formed as the supercontinent of Pangaea began to break up. So at Lyme Regis we see cliffs made of dark shales, clays and muddy limestones deposited in marine environments that began to teem with life. Fossils in the rocks have helped us build a picture of the wonderful variety of life in these ancient biomes, and the inexorable erosion of the coastline is constantly revealing more and more of them. Lyme Regis and its near neighbour Charmouth are the fossil centres of the Jurassic Coast. Their dark, crumbly cliffs are packed with the remains of all kinds of creatures and, since the sea will only eventually wash them away, we are encouraged to search the shoreline for them. For expert advice on where to look and what to look for go to Charmouth Heritage Centre or Lyme Regis Museum; both organise regular fossil hunting walks led by knowledgeable and enthusiastic experts.

Above: A fossil Nautilus on Monmouth Beach, Lyme Regis. They are not ammonites and there are some species still alive today.

These rocks (inset picture) at the western end of Monmouth Beach are known as the Blue Lias and consist of alternating bands of shales and muddy limestones. The limestones are more resistant to erosion and form ledges that stretch out to sea. Many ammonites can be seen in these ledges and in one place (only visible at low tide) there are so many that it is known as the 'ammonite graveyard'. Maybe some change in the conditions in the ocean caused many to die quite suddenly.

The rocks of Charmouth and Lyme Regis are from the Lower Jurassic, sometimes known as the Lias. These clays, marls (clays containing a significant amount of calcium carbonate) and limestones form very unstable cliffs that are receding rapidly and constantly revealing more of their numerous fossils. In the middle of the photograph stands Golden Cap, at 191 metres the highest cliff on the south coast of England. Its name derives from the top layers of the Cretaceous Greensand Formation, in recent years not so 'golden' due to the increased vegetation. You may think this is odd, where is the rest of the Jurassic? This is another exposure of the Great Unconformity (see page 37).

Golden Sandstones

The cliffs at West Bay are much photographed, particularly when the early or setting sun adds a golden glow to the already spectacular strata. These are the Bridport Sands, still Lower Jurassic in age and probably deposited in a large river delta that slowly built southwards into the Jurassic sea. It is quite easy to see fossilised worm burrows in the sandstones at the foot of the cliffs and in fallen material, further confirmation that these are shallow water deposits. Be very careful near the cliffs, rock falls are common. The cliffs have a ribbed appearance due to the regular layers of harder sandstones, harder because they have been cemented by the relatively high amount of calcium carbonate they contain. The calcium carbonate comes from the shells of marine creatures and it might be that the layers with relatively large amounts represent quieter times when less detrital material was being deposited. If so, it is clear this happened on a regular cyclical basis and may relate to climate changes brought about by a natural cycle such as the shift of the Earth's axis. It may come as a surprise to learn that the sandstones are not in fact golden coloured but rather grey or bluey grey. It is only on the surface where the iron content is oxidised that they appear golden.

Above: East Cliff, West Bay in morning sunshine. Even at this distance the harder sandstone layers stand out. You may find this cliff familiar; at the time of writing West Bay is the setting for the television drama 'Broadchurch'.

The Great Unconformity

Sedimentary rocks are typically laid down in horizontal layers on the sea bed. We now see sedimentary layers on land, perhaps millions of years after they were deposited in an ancient ocean. The land is constantly being eroded and over time earth movements, associated with the inexorable movement of the plates of the Earth's crust, may result in eroded sediments being once more under the sea. Further sedimentary layers may then be deposited on top, and in due course the whole sequence may become land once more. There may be a time gap of millions of years between two consecutive layers having been deposited, but someone looking at the sequence may think they were formed in the same ocean, one directly after the other. The fossil record in the layers may indicate there is a time difference between their formation, but there may be other, more obvious ways to tell. If the older layers have been subject to earth movements they may have been folded or at least tilted, and when younger layers are laid down on top, they will lie at a different angle to the older layers.

This is the situation we find on the Jurassic Coast; in the cliffs east of Lyme Regis we see tilted Lower and Upper Jurassic strata directly overlain by horizontal Cretaceous strata, all of them deposited in the sea. The entire Upper Jurassic sequence is missing; this doesn't mean it was never deposited, rather that, following the Upper Jurassic, this area was land for millions of years and all the Upper Jurassic rocks were eroded, before the sea returned again in the Cretaceous Period. In East Devon the entire Jurassic sequence has been eroded and the Cretaceous layers rest directly on red Triassic rocks.

Above: The Great Unconformity. Golden Cap is in the middle picture with its cap of Cretaceous Greensand unconformably overlying Lower Jurassic sediments.

Chesil Beach

The Fleet at Rodden Hive.

The Ice Ages, particularly the last one which ended just over ten thousand years ago, have played a major part in shaping Britain's landscape. This is not only true of those areas which were covered by glaciers and ice sheets; Dorset was a little way south of the furthest extension of the ice but has felt the effects of climate changes associated with the Ice Ages and changes in sea level as ice sheets melted and reformed elsewhere. The formation of Chesil Beach was a result of such fluctuations. This eighteen mile long shingle storm beach only reached its present form about five thousand years ago. It has formed via a process known as 'longshore drift', prevailing westerly winds and currents have transported sand and shingle eastwards along the coast, pushing it onshore and forming a barrier beach. After the last ice melted the sea level rose and huge quantities of sandy material were eroded from the area of Lyme Bay and as the sea level continued to rise the beach was pushed further north and east. A great deal of this material may have come from large meltwater rivers that flowed from the retreating ice sheets to the north.

It has been suggested that Chesil Beach was fully formed about 7-5000 years ago, but mainly consisted of sandy material, not the pebbles we see today. Finally, old cliffs which had previously been stranded inland by falling sea levels during the Ice Age, now came into the reach of the waves again, resulting in much coarser material being transported eastwards and covering the beach in the pebbles. The material that made Chesil Beach has long been exhausted and it can now only decline.

It is something of a myth that the pebbles gradually increase in size as you follow it eastwards from West Bay. It is certainly true that the pebbles are generally much smaller at the western end of the beach and relatively large at the Portland end, and it is still something of a mystery why this is so. It may be that the greater surface area of large pebbles enabled them to be carried further.

The World's Best Building Stone - The Isle of Portland

Look at the quarried rock surfaces around Pulpit Rock on Portland Bill and you will see numerous fossil oysters. These molluscs have survived largely unchanged for millions of years and are found living on the bottom of shallow seas, typically near the coast. This is one clue that the Portland limestones were deposited in a shallow water marine environment not far from land. Another clue is the fact that some of the limestones in the Portland Series are 'oolitic'. They consist of tiny round grains of calcium carbonate cemented together. Such a deposit is forming today in the shallow, tropical seas near

the Bahamas. Here the calcium carbonate precipitates around small shell fragments or sand particles and is rolled backwards and forwards by wave action, ensuring the grains are spherical. At times the environment was stable enough for thick, homogeneous layers of limestone to form; this, coupled with the relatively high calcium carbonate content ensuring a hard final rock, has made the Portland Stone an excellent building material.

Portland Stone has been quarried at Portland since Roman times, but it was in the seventeenth century when demand really grew thanks to the need to rebuild London after the Great Fire. The industry peaked in the nineteenth century when the railways made export of the stone easier.

Main picture: Thick layers of Portland Stone on the east coast of Portland near Portland Bill. The gently seaward sloping layers of the limestone enabled it to be quarried and taken out to ships waiting offshore. Small cranes known as 'whims' (top of cliffs in picture) lifted the stone to boats which were then rowed out to the ships.
Inset picture: Fossil oysters in the Portland Stone near Pulpit Rock.

Oil Shales and Dangerous Ledges

Kimmeridge is another classic location on the Jurassic Coast. Its layers of shales, clays and limestones are similar to those of Lyme Regis, but younger, being Upper Jurassic in age and having formed up to 50 million years later than the Lower Jurassic rocks of Lyme Bay. The sequence here is known as the Kimmeridge Clay and the rocks again formed in a marine environment rich in life and are consequently full of fossils. It is not permitted to collect fossils here but a local man, Steve Etches, has built up a remarkable collection which is now on public display in a museum in Kimmeridge. As well as the ubiquitous ammonites it showcases specimens of the wonderful large marine reptiles that thrived in the Jurassic seas. The shore at Kimmeridge is, however, a good place to "collect" fossils with your camera; the rocks are often littered with ammonites and you may be lucky to spot remains of the bones of marine reptiles (see photo 4 page 21).

The harder, gently dipping bands of limestone stand out in the cliffs and, being more resistant to erosion than the shales, form hard ledges which stretch out to sea. These have long been a hazard to ships.

The Kimmeridge Clays are the source rocks for the North Sea oil reserves. Under the North Sea these strata are deeply buried and this has created the right conditions for oil to form from the high organic content of the sediments. This high organic content is a result of conditions on the sea floor where the sediments were forming. Dead organisms would normally decay given sufficient oxygen, but the lower levels of these ancient seas were clearly poor in oxygen, perhaps a result of a lack of circulation as is thought to be the case in the Black Sea today. Additionally, the warm, tropical Jurassic seas would have been teeming with plankton which, as they died and sank to the bottom, would have formed a mud rich in organic material. Incidentally the small oil well at Kimmeridge is not extracting oil from the Kimmeridge Clays but from older Jurassic sediments buried more deeply here.

The Structure of the Isle of Purbeck

Chalk

Arish Me

At Winspit on the Isle of Purbeck the Portland limestone strata are horizontal.

All strata dip steeply to the north

Wealden Series

Worbarrow Bay

Portland and Purbeck limestones

This view was taken from the Chalk ridge overlooking Arish Mell. Beyond that is Worbarrow Bay with the cliffs formed of the relatively hard Portland and Purbeck limestones on the extreme right. Between the limestones and the Chalk ridge lies the valley formed mostly out of the softer Cretaceous sediments known as the Wealden Series. These are sands and clays largely deposited in river deltas. This structure continues eastwards through the Isle of Purbeck to the coast at Swanage where the valley of the softer sediments is considerably wider. Note that as the coastline sweeps to the south beyond Kimmeridge we see the Portland and Purbeck limestones lying horizontally, part of a broad monocline or step-like fold in the strata caused by the earth movements that built the mountains of the Alps.

The Gateway Towns

The 'Gateway Towns' along the Jurassic Coast are, strictly speaking, not part of the world heritage site, but convenient places from where it can be accessed and where there are museums and information centres.

Exmouth, on the east bank of the estuary of the River Exe, is perhaps the oldest seaside resort in Devon and is where Orcombe Point marks the western end of the Jurassic Coast. Here the 'Geoneedle' officially denotes the start of the site and represents all the different types of sediments found along the coast. **Budleigh Salterton** is a charming seaside town and home to the famous Pebble Beds that we have met earlier. It also boasts a nature reserve along the banks of the River Otter which reaches the sea here. The Fairlynch Museum is located in a pretty thatched building and has a local geology collection. **Sidmouth** is another popular resort with an attractive Regency front nestling in a gap between impressive red sandstone cliffs. Sidmouth Museum offers a comprehensive display on the Jurassic Coast and local geology. A few miles further east the little village of **Beer** presents a shingle beach protected by cliffs of the easternmost outcrop of the Chalk. Here, a variety of the white rock makes a very good building stone and the quarries that once produced Beer Stone provide a fascinating visitor experience. **Seaton** is next door to Beer and a major fault sees the return of red sandstone. Between here and **Lyme Regis** however the desert sandstones give way to marine sediments, the start of the Jurassic rocks full of fossils of the wonderful marine life that evolved in the Jurassic oceans. Lyme is a fascinating, historic town and, with its neighbour **Charmouth,** an ideal place for fossil collecting. The museum at Lyme and the Charmouth Heritage Centre have excellent displays and also organise and lead fossil hunting trips.

The dark clays and shales give way to golden sandstone at **West Bay,** the harbour for **Bridport**. There is another interesting museum here while the harbour itself provides a pretty location to sit by or wander around. Sitting behind Chesil Beach and at the start of the Fleet lagoon, **Abbotsbury** is a picturesque village built of the local Jurassic limestone. Once a major monastic centre, it is littered with enigmatic remains of the ancient abbey. Nearby are wonderful viewing places from which to appreciate Chesil Beach and the Fleet. **Weymouth** is the largest town on the Jurassic Coast and a major tourist destination ever since George III holidayed here. It has an impressive Georgian seafront with views over the nearby Isle of Portland. The next stop eastwards along the coast is **Lulworth,** where the almost circular bay and its calm, shallow waters attracts thousands of visitors. Again, the Heritage Centre has an excellent display on local geology. Near the eastern end of the Jurassic Coast sits the Victorian seaside town of **Swanage**, its bay cut out of the soft, Wealden Series sands and clays, sandwiched between the Chalk and the Portland and Purbeck limestones. Swanage, too, has a museum, delightfully situated on the front and with interesting displays on geology. Although slightly inland on the River Frome, **Wareham** is regarded as a gateway town and its historic quayside is well worth a visit.

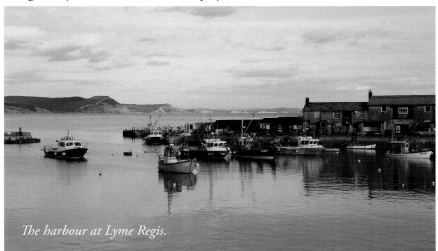
The harbour at Lyme Regis.

Lulworth Cove.

The harbour at West Bay.

Wareham Quay.

The Tithe Barn at Abbotsbury.

Museums and Heritage Centres

Fairlynch Museum, Budleigh Salterton, EX9 6NO, 01395442666

Sidmouth Museum, EX10 8LY, 01395 516139

Town Museum, Lyme Regis, DT7 3QA, 01297 443370

Charmouth Heritage Centre, DT6 6LE, 01297 560772

Bridport Museum, DT6 3RJ, 01308 458703

Portland Museum, DT5 1HS, 01305 821804

Lulworth Heritage Centre, BH20 5RQ, 01929 400587

The Etches Collection, Kimmeridge, BH20 5PE, 01929 270000

Durlston Visitor Centre, Swanage, BH19 2JL, 01929 424443

Langton Matravers Museum, Purbeck, BH19 3HZ, 01929 423168

Swanage Museum and Heritage Centre, BH19 2LJ, 01929 421427

Dorset County Museum, Dorchester, DT1 1XA, 01305 262735

Further reading and bibliography

Fossils and Rocks of the Jurassic Coast, Robert Westwood, Inspiring Places Publishing, 5th edition, 2014
Jurassic Coast Fossils, Robert Westwood, Inspiring Places Publishing, 2015
Geology of the Jurassic Coast - The Red Coast Revealed, Richard A Edwards, Coastal Publishing, 2008
Geology of the Jurassic Coast - The Isle of Purbeck, Paul Ensom and Malcolm Turnbull, Coastal Publishing, 2011
The Official Guide to the Jurassic Coast, edited by Professor Denys Brunsden, Coastal Publishing, 2003